The Rain

Written by Lesley Jane
Illustrated by Craig Smith

It started to rain. The rain hit the ground.
The rain hit the trees, and the rain hit
Grandad's roof.

3

There was a hole in the roof,
so the rain hit Grandad.
It hit him on the nose, and he woke up.
Grandad put a pot under the drip.
He went to sleep in the chair.

There was another hole in the roof,
so the rain dripped on Grandad.
Grandad put a boot under the drip.
He went to sleep in the bathtub.

There was another hole in the roof,
and the rain dripped on Grandad.
He put a bucket under the drip.
"I will sleep under the table," said Grandad.

9

It rained and rained.
The water came up the steps,
but Grandad slept on.

The water came across the porch,
but Grandad slept on.

The water came under the table,
and Grandad got wet.
"Help!" said Grandad.

Then Bob came in his boat.
He rowed up to the porch
and called to Grandad.
Bob and Grandad rowed
across the fields.